40 Romantic-Era
40 Romantic-Era Composers
for Easy Classical Guitar

Cover image by Charles-François Daubigny (1817–1878)

Arranged and edited by Mark Phillips

ISBN: 9798727802250

A. J. Cornell Publications

CONTENTS

Theme

(from Variations for String Quartet, Op. 17)

by Juan Crisóstomo de Arriaga

4

Lento sostenuto
(from Preludes & Lessons, Op. 33)

by Sterndale Bennett

Ode to Joy

(from Symphony No. 9, Fourth Movement)

by Ludwig van Beethoven

Moderately fast

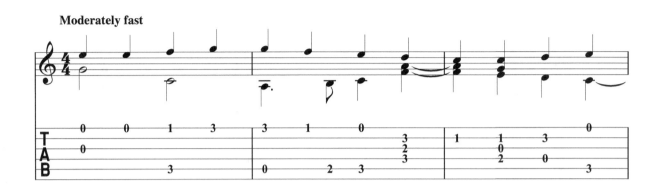

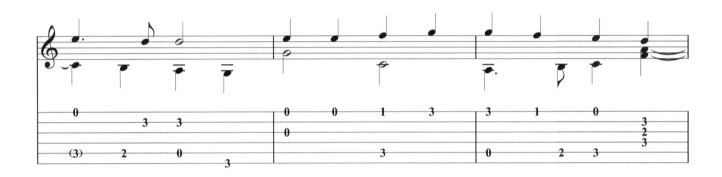

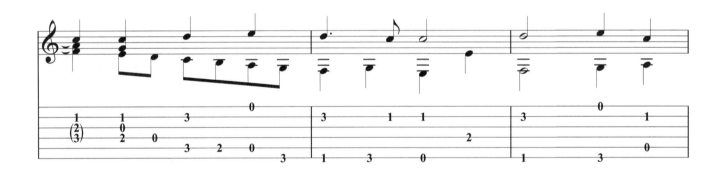

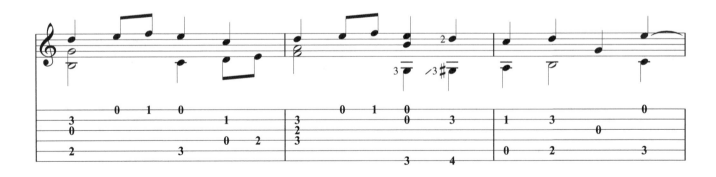

The Shepherds' Farewell

(from *L'enfance du Christ*)

by Hector Berlioz

Moderately

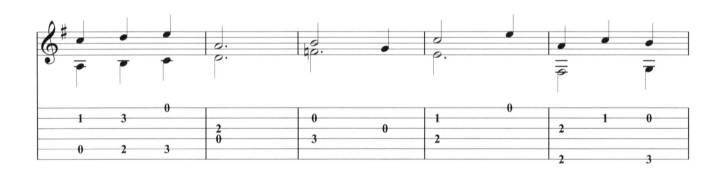

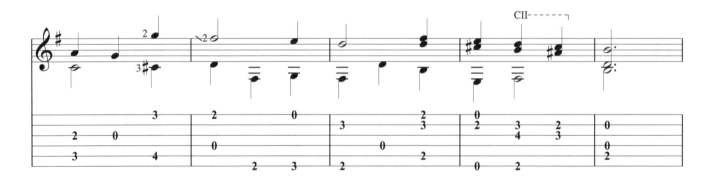

Les Dragons d'Alcala

(from Carmen Suite No. 1)

by Georges Bizet

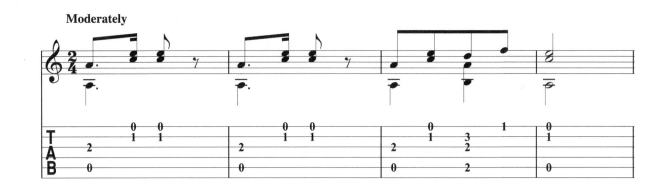

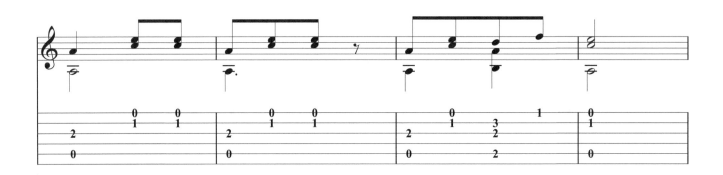

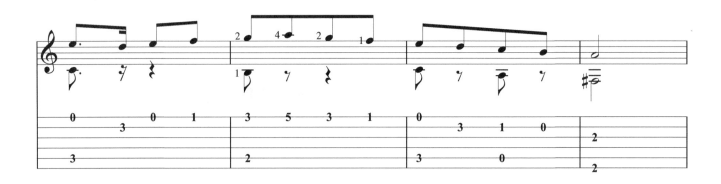

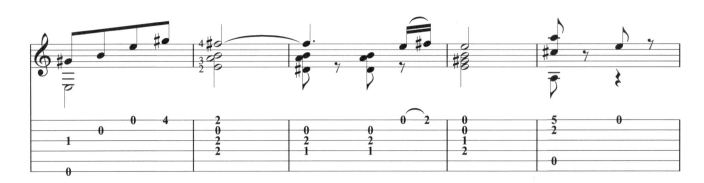

Trio
(from Paraphrases: "Mazurka")

by Aleksandr Borodin

Moderately bright

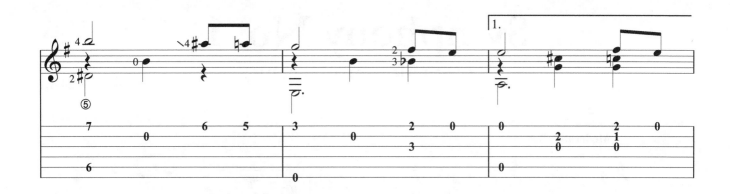

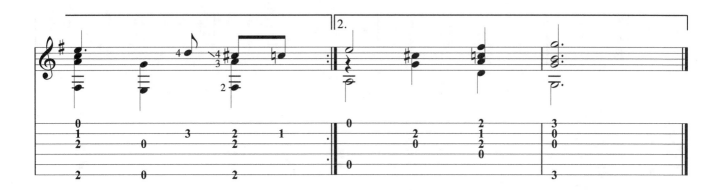

Symphony No. 1
(Fourth Movement Theme)

by Johannes Brahms

Moderately fast

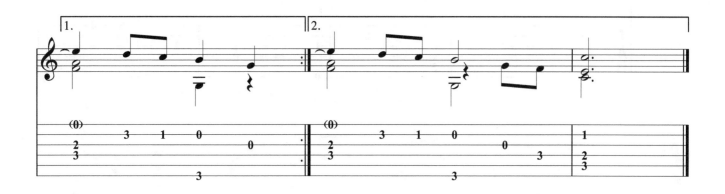

Cantabile
(B. 84)

by Frédéric Chopin

Study No. 82
(from 100 Progressive Studies, Op. 139)

by Carl Czerny

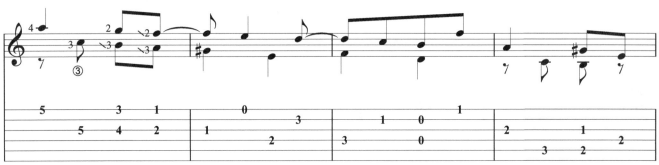

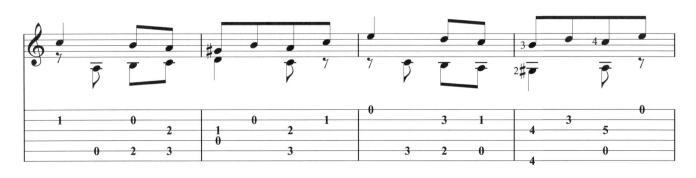

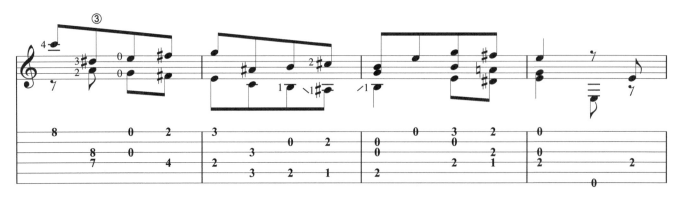

Slavonic Dance
(Op. 72, No. 2; Excerpt)

by Antonín Dvořák

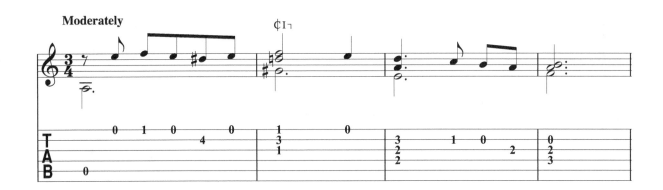

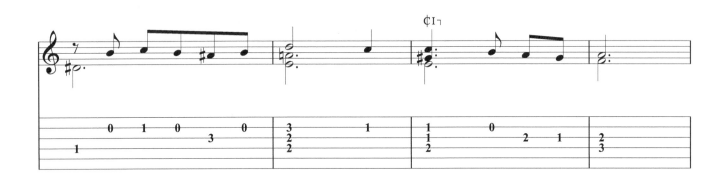

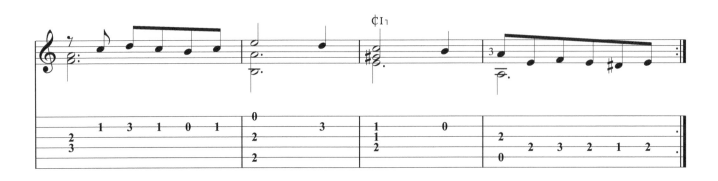

Pomp and Circumstance
(Op. 39, No. 1)

by Edward Elgar

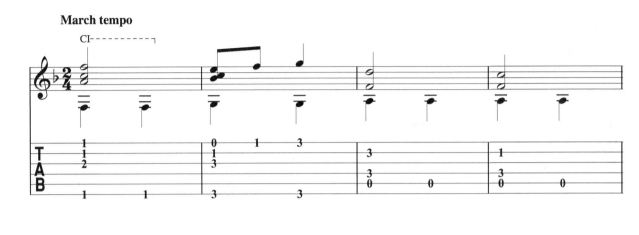

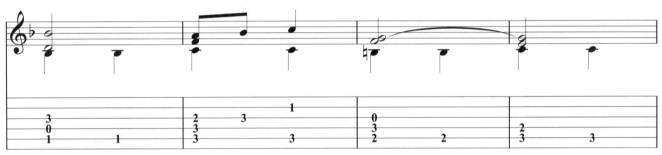

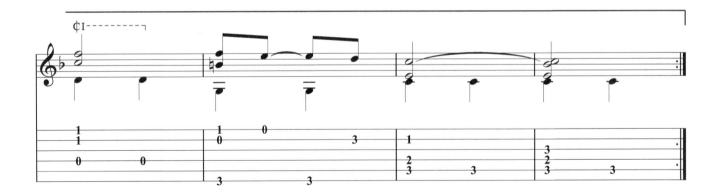

Nocturne No. 8

(H 30; Excerpt)

by John Field

Prelude

(from *Prélude, Fugue et Variation*, Op. 18; Excerpt)

by César Franck

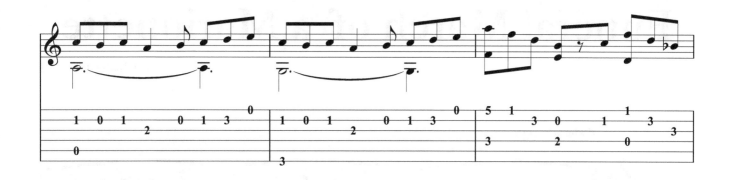

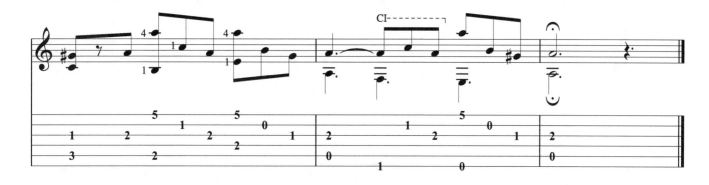

Funeral March of a Marionette

by Charles Gounod

Gratitude
(Op. 62, No. 2; Excerpt)

by Edvard Grieg

Moderately

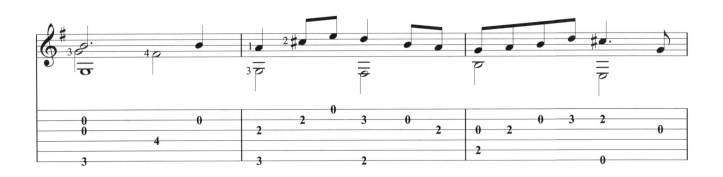

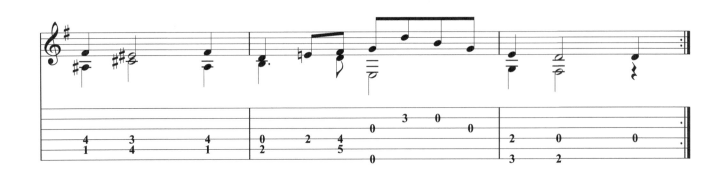

Liebestraum
(Notturno No. 3)

by Franz Liszt

Moderately fast

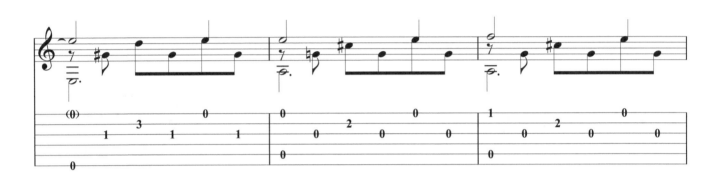

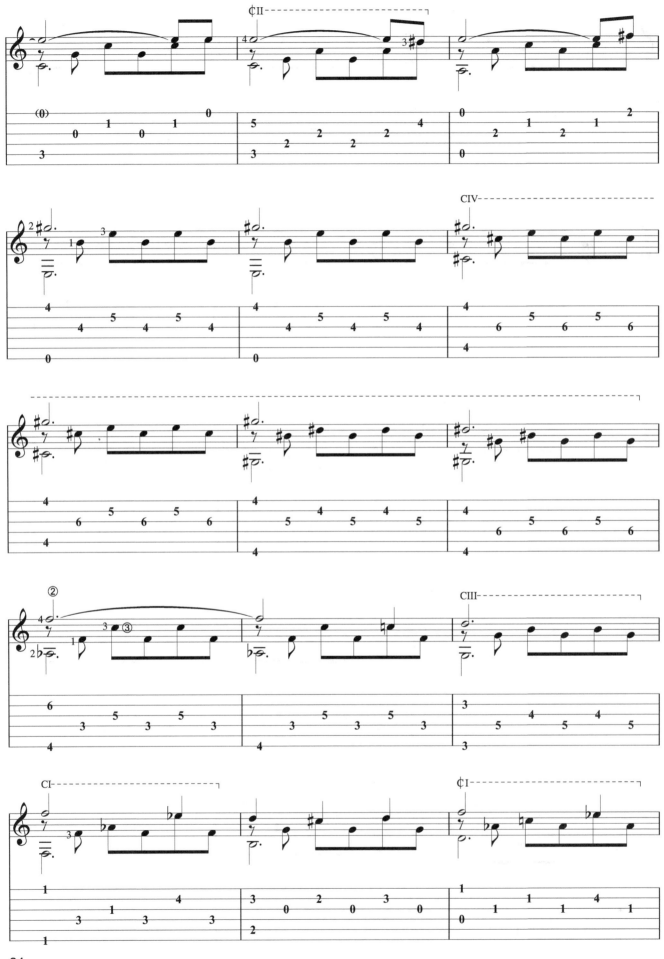

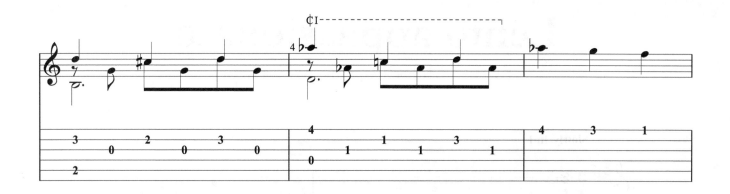

D.S. al Coda

𝄌 **Coda**

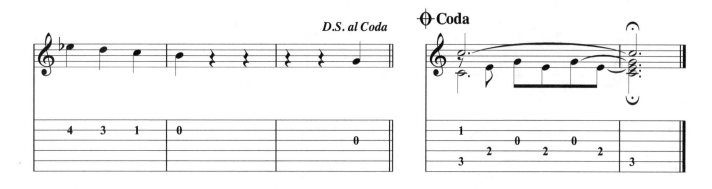

Lento appassionato

(from 3 Mélodies, Op. 5; Excerpt)

by Fanny Mendelssohn

Wedding March

(from *A Midsummer Night's Dream*)

by Felix Mendelssohn

Moderately fast

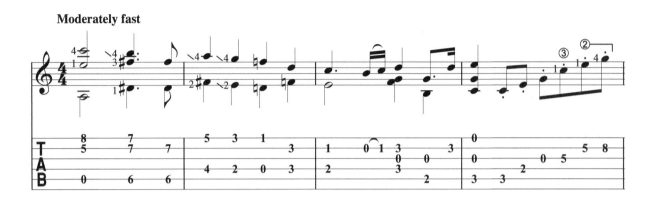

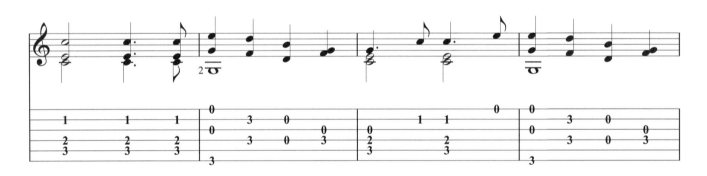

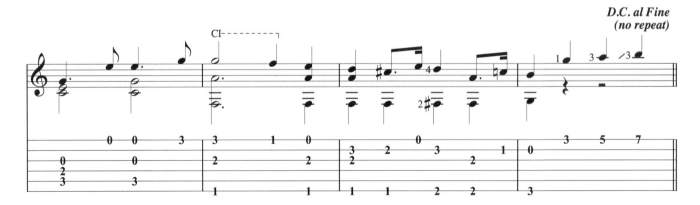

Elegy

(from *5 Serenaden für die Jugend,* Op. 183)

by Carl Reinecke

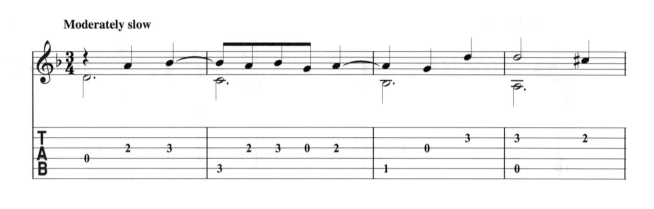

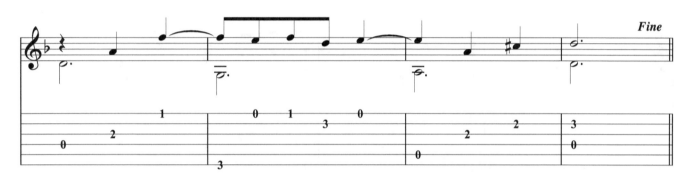

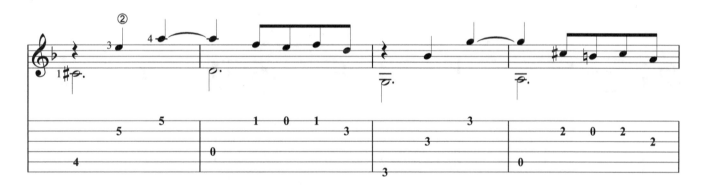

Preghiera
(from *Dinorah*)

by Giacomo Meyerbeer

Moderately, in 2

Copyright © 2021 A. J. Cornell Publications

41

Spanish Dance No. 2
(from 5 Spanish Dances, Op. 12)

by Moritz Moszkowski

D.C. al Fine
(take repeat)

Une larme
(A Teardrop)

by Modest Mussorgsky

La Chaconne
(from *Monsieur et Madame Denis*)

by Jacques Offenbach

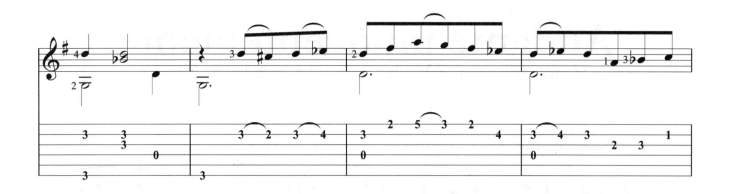

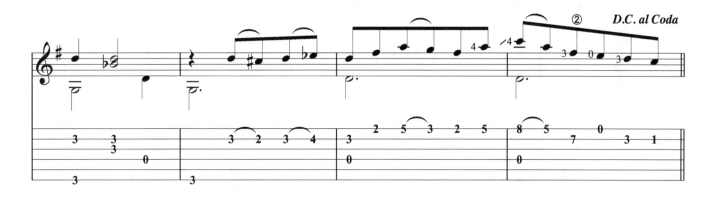

D.C. al Coda

Coda

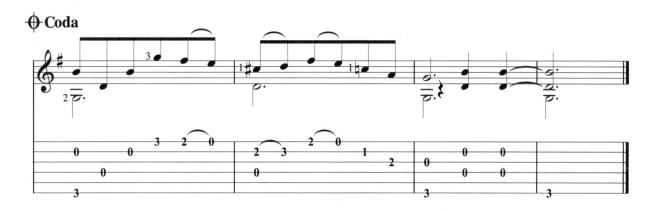

Andante innocentemente

(from Sonata for Violin and Guitar, Op. 3, No. 6)

by Nicolò Paganini

Moderately slow

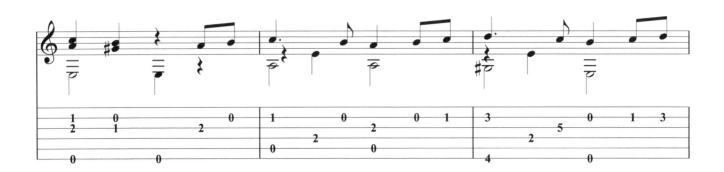

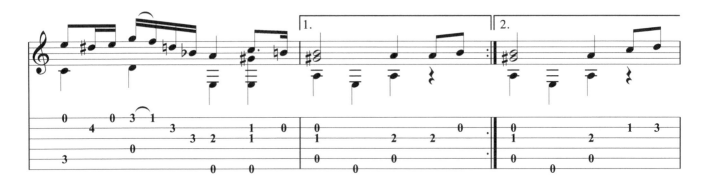

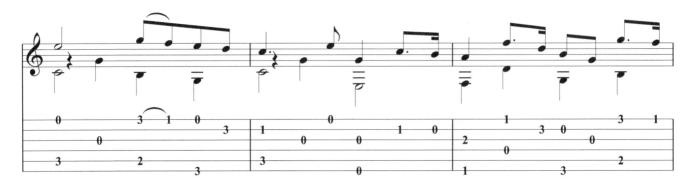

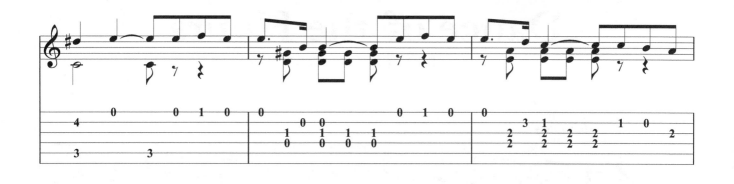

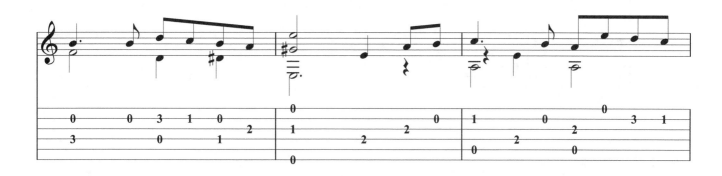

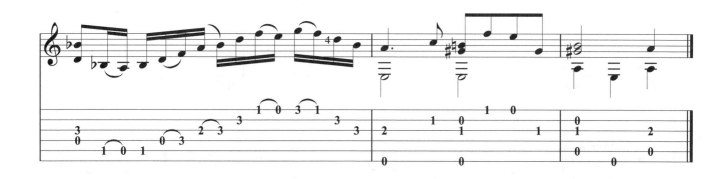

Dance of the Hours

(from *La Gioconda*)

by Amilcare Ponchielli

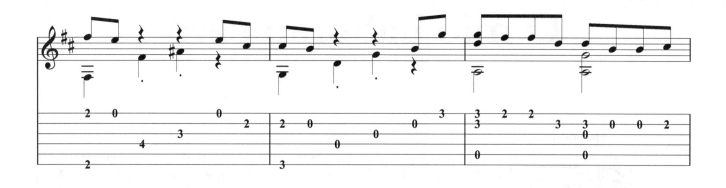

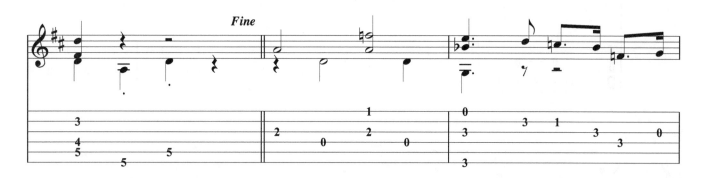

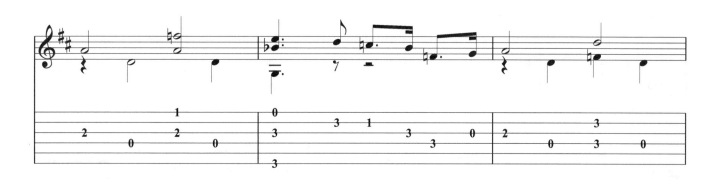

O mio babbino caro

(from *Gianni Schicchi*)

by Giacomo Puccini

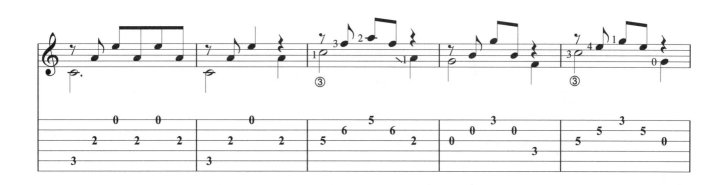

Minuetto
(from Horn Trio No. 14, Op. 82)

by Anton Reicha

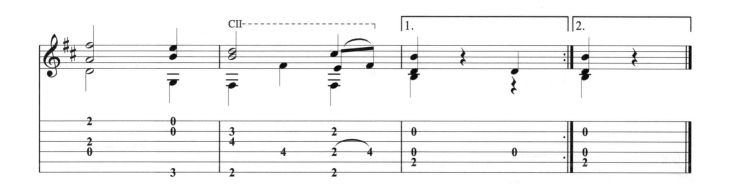

The Kalendar Prince

(from *Scheherazade*)

by Nikolai Rimsky-Korsakov

Moderately fast

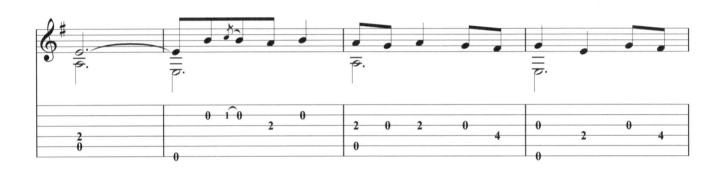

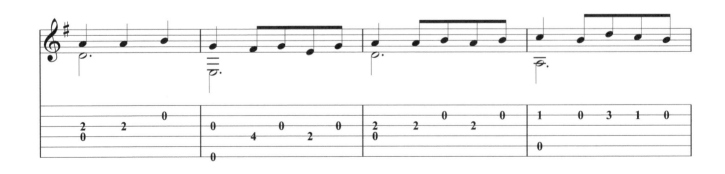

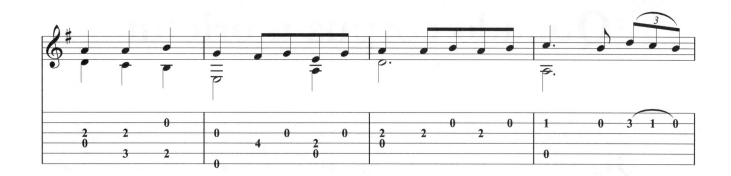

Quando corpus morietur

(from Stabat Mater; Excerpt)

by Gioachino Rossini

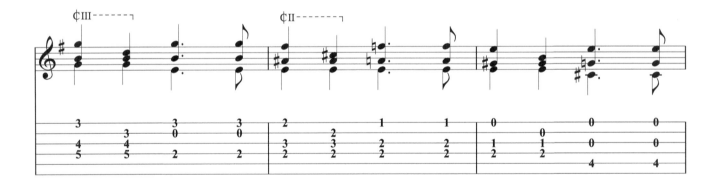

Melody in F

by Anton Rubinstein

*Original key: F major; this arrangement in C major for playability.

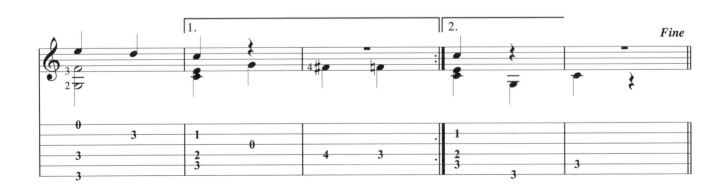

D.C. al Fine
(take 2nd ending)

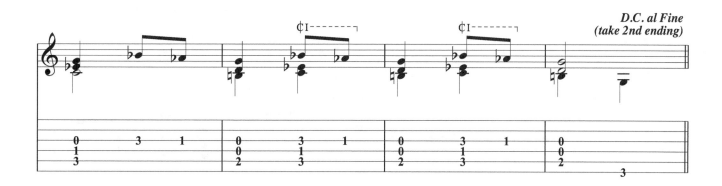

Ave Maria
(from 20 Motets)

by Camille Saint-Saëns

Impromptu
(Op. posth. 142, No. 3; Excerpt)

by Franz Schubert

Romance No. 1
(from *Drei Romanzen,* Op. 21)

by Clara Schumann

Of Foreign Lands and People

(from *Scenes from Childhood*)

by Robert Schumann

Moderately slow, in 2

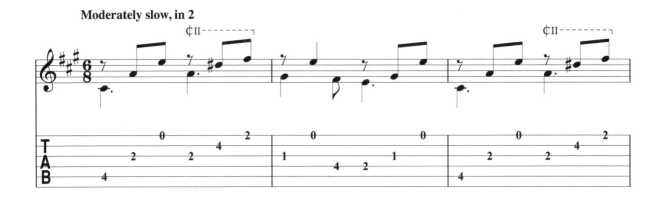

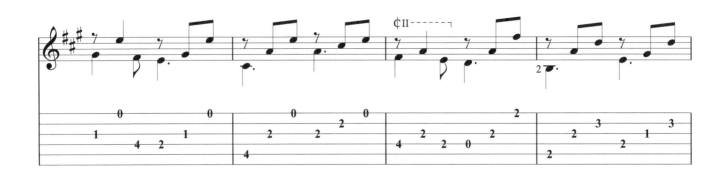

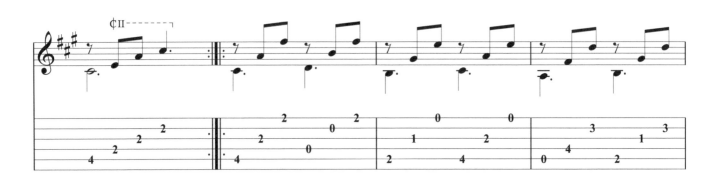

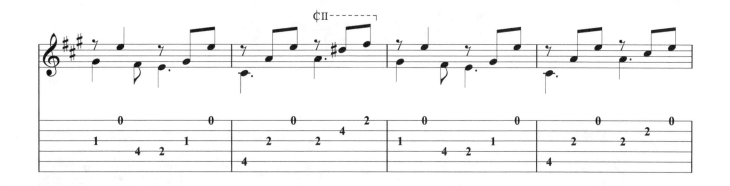

L'Innocence
(from Bagatelles and Impromptus, JB 1:19)

by Bedřich Smetana

Romance No. 2
(Op. 255)

by Johann Strauss Jr.

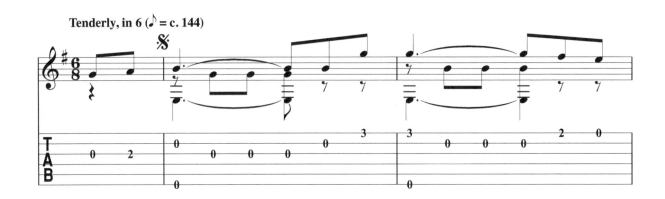

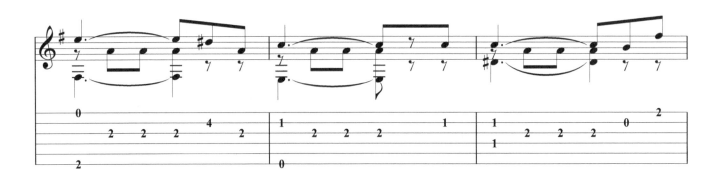

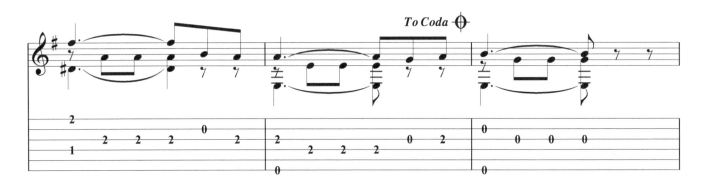

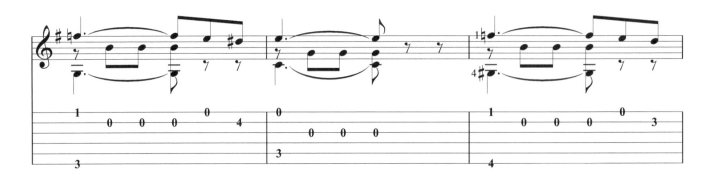

D.S. al Coda

Coda

Dance of the Sugar Plum Fairy

(from *The Nutcracker*)

by Pyotr Il'yich Tchaikovsky

Moderately slow, in 2

*Sound note w/ L.H. finger

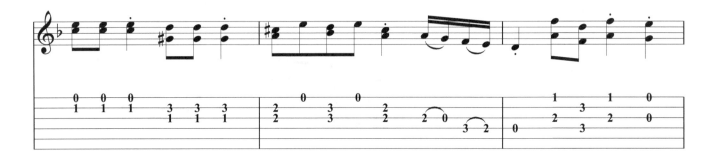

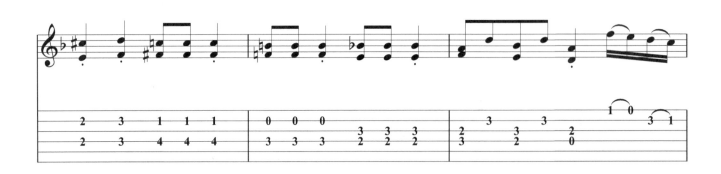

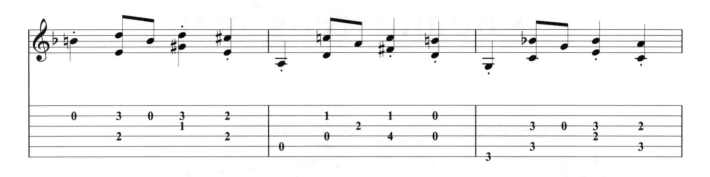

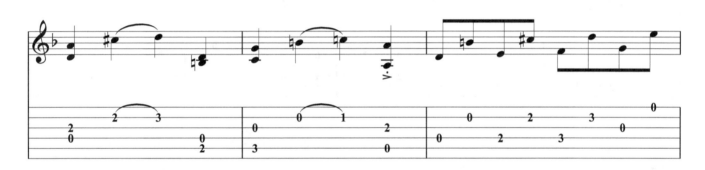

Andante religioso
(Op. 70)

by Francis Thomé

Prologue

(from *Simon Boccanegra*)

by Giuseppe Verdi

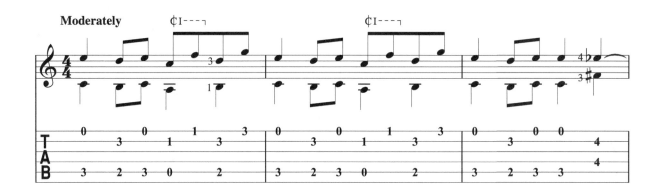

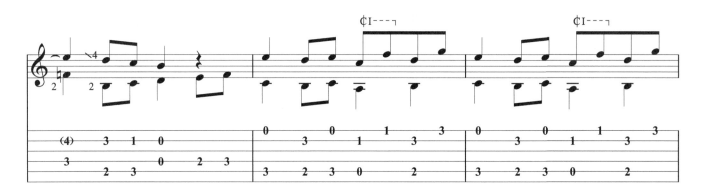

Bridal Chorus

(from *Lohengrin*)

by Richard Wagner